HORRID HENRY'S DOUBLE DARE

Francesca Simon spent her childhood on the beach in California, and then went to Yale and Oxford Universities to study medieval history and literature. She now lives in London with her English husband and their son. When she is not writing books she is doing theatre and restaurant reviews or chasing after her Tibetan Spaniel, Shanti.

Tony Ross is one of Britain's best known illustrators, with many picture books to his name as well as line drawings for many fiction titles. He lives in Nottinghamshire.

Complete list of Horrid Henry
titles at the end of the book

Also by Francesca Simon

Don't Cook Cinderella
Helping Hercules

and for younger readers

Don't Be Horrid, Henry
Horrid Henry's Birthday Party

HORRID HENRY'S

DOUBLE DARE

Francesca Simon

Illustrated by Tony Ross

Orion
Children's Books

First published in Great Britain in 2009
by Orion Children's Books
a division of the Orion Publishing Group Ltd
Orion House
5 Upper St Martin's Lane
London WC2H 9EA
An Hachette UK company

1 3 5 7 9 10 8 6 4 2

A catalogue record for this book
is available from the British Library

Printed in Great Britain
by Clays Ltd, St Ives plc

ISBN 978 1 4440 0008 5

www.horridhenry.co.uk
www.orionbooks.co.uk

CONTENTS

THE PURPLE HAND RULES

The Purple Hand Club is the best
club ever. Naturally, everyone
wants to join. Well they can't. No
girls allowed and no wormy toad
little brothers - by order of me, the
Lord High Excellent Majesty of the
Purple Hand. Unless... Unless...
Well, maybe some people can EARN
their membership. They
have to be bold. They
have to be brave. And
most of all they have to
give me LOADS OF
SWEETS.

   We've got the scariest
dares and sneakiest
jokes - brilliant for
April Fool's Day,

1

or for tricking mean, horrible parents, smelly crybaby brothers and sisters, and bossy-boots girls all year round. We also know all the best jokes, tee hee!
P.S. Don't even bother reading Frog-Face Margaret's copycat book – it'll just make you feel sick.

PETER: Henry, please can I join your club?

NO WAY, WORM. Well, okay, 'cause I'm so nice...

I DARE YOU TO:

• Sneak into Mum's box of chocolates, pinch her favourite Double Chocolate Nutty Surprise and bring it to me.

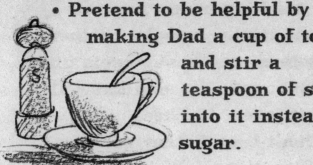

- Pretend to be helpful by making Dad a cup of tea and stir a teaspoon of salt into it instead of sugar.

- Stand outside in the street for an hour, holding a sign that says 'I AM A WORM'.

PETER: But everyone will laugh at me.

Too right, worm.

PETER: But I hate being laughed at.

Tough, you can't be in the Purple Hand Club. Why don't you go to

that old grouch face
Margaret's book. She
might let you join
her baby club.

Ha. He's gone.
Now I can tell you
my best little
brother jokes!

*Do you know why my little brother is built
upside down?*

Because his nose runs
and his feet smell!

**PETER: Mum!
Henry said my
feet smell!**

GET LOST!

How do you know if it's raining?
Push your little brother outside and see
if he comes in wet.

Mum: Why won't you play
football with Peter?
Henry: I'm bored of kicking him around.

Dad: Don't be selfish, Henry. Let Peter use
the sledge half the time.
Henry: I do, Dad. I use it going down
the hill and I let him use it coming up!

Mummy Monster: What are you doing with
that saw and where's your little brother?
Young Monster: He's only my half-
brother now! Ha ha!

Miss Battle-Axe: Henry, if you had ten
sweets and Peter asked you for one, how
many sweets would you have then?
Henry: Ten!

PETER: Your jokes are horrid, Henry.

No, they aren't. Henry rules!

MORE OF HENRY'S HORRIBLE TRICKS

- If your little brother or sister is watching TV and you want to watch something really great, like *Rapper Zapper* or *Gross-Out*, tell them that Mum and Dad want to see them – urgently. As soon as they're out of the room, grab the remote!

- Tell your mum that your little brother or sister has been scratching their head all day. Your mum will think they've

got nits – and send to
them to the Nit
Nurse, or torture
them with the nit
comb for hours. Tee hee.

- Hide your mum or dad's glasses or car
keys. When they've searched
everywhere, pretend to find them. Your
mum and dad will think you are very
clever and let you watch TV all night,
or give you loads of sweets as a reward.

- Hold a jumble sale
and put your little
brother or sister up for
sale. Warning: you
might not get paid
very much money but
it's better than having
them bug you all day.

- Take your dad's favourite CD out of its case and replace it with something really good of your own. Watch while he relaxes in his chair, ready to listen to his boring old CD and the Killer Boy Rats boom out!

RUDE RALPH'S REVOLTING TRICKS, JOKES AND DARES

Hey Ralph, I bet you know some super-rude tricks and jokes, guaranteed to make all prissy toads run away screaming.

RALPH: Yeah, how about these really revolting dares?

9

RALPH'S RUDE AND REVOLTING DARES

- Dare your friend to kiss four bare legs and a bare bottom. (All this really means is that they have to kiss a chair, but don't tell them that!)

- Dare a prissy girl to smell the feet of everyone in the room and put them in order from best to worst.

Bet mine are the BEST. They smell like the stinkiest cheese ever.

- During school dinner, shout out something stupid, like 'I LOVE MY TEACHER!'

- Tell a very rude joke to your teacher. Teachers love rude jokes.

YEAH! Go Ralph!

RALPH'S RUDE JOKES

Who shouted 'knickers' at the Big Bad Wolf?
Little Rude Riding Hood.

What did the traffic lights say to the car?
Don't look at me, I'm changing.

*What do you get if you cross
a skunk with a dinosaur?*
A stinkasaurus.

*What do you call an elephant that never
washes?*
A smellyphant.

What flies through the air and stinks?
A smelly-copter.

*What do you do if you
find a python in your
toilet?*
Wait until he's finished.

*What happens when
the queen burps?*
She issues a royal
pardon.

MOODY MARGARET: We don't want nappy-face Peter in our club either.

RUDE RALPH: Hey Peter, if you give me your pocket money, I'll make Henry let you join the Purple Hand Club.

RUDE RALPH'S POCKET MONEY PRANKS

RUDE RALPH: If you've got some money buy a whoopee cushion and some magic soot. They'll be your best buys ever.

- Use the whoopee cushion at home when your mum and dad have some important guests round for dinner. Everyone will really enjoy your trick because it'll liven up their boring evening.

- Sprinkle the magic soot on your living room carpet. This joke works best when your carpet has just been hoovered!

14

NEW NICK'S TASKS

RUDE RALPH: Hey Henry, Nick wants to join the Purple Hand Club.

No way! Wait a minute, what if he's got loads of sweets to give us. Let's give him three tasks to do and if he succeeds, we'll let him join.

THE PURPLE HAND CLUB TASKS

I, Henry, Lord High Excellent Majesty of the Purple Hand Club do declare that the following tasks be undertaken by Nick in order to become a member of the best club ever.

Henry

1. Before Miss Battle-Axe enters the classroom in the morning, sneak a plastic spider on her chair. You will only pass this task if (a) nobody spots you with the spider, and (b) Miss Battle-Axe runs out of the room screaming!

MOODY MARGARET:
I'm going to tell on you!

2. During class, put up your
hand and ask a very interesting
question, like, 'Do you like peanut
butter sandwiches?' or 'Did Queen
Victoria ever ask you round to tea?' You
will only pass this task if Miss Battle-Axe
looks at you as though you are a total
worm and gets VERY angry.

3. At lunchtime, complain to Greasy Greta,
the Demon Dinner Lady, that the custard is
cold and lumpy. You will only pass this task
if you still manage to get some dinner!

LATER...

NEW NICK: I've done
all three tasks. Can I
be in the Purple
Hand Club now?

Got any sweets?

**NEW NICK: Loads!
Just not on me.**

No sweets, eh? The penalty is...

THREE MORE PURPLE HAND CLUB TASKS

**I, Henry,
Leader of the
Purple Hand
Club order you
to do three
more tasks.**

Henry

1. Swap one of the goodies in Greedy Graham's lunchbox for something healthy from yours – and scoff it up before he finds out.

2. Muddle up two people's names, and call them the wrong names all day.

18

The two people have to be – Margaret and Susan.

3. Write a fake love letter from Gorgeous Gurinder to Beefy Bert.

> To my Handsome Bert
>
> Lovely Bert
> You are as beefy
> as can be
> Would you like
> To come to tea?
>
> Gurinder xx

RUDE RALPH:
Nice one, Henry!

LATER...

NEW NICK: I've
done all three
tasks. Can I join
the Purple Hand
Club now?

Nearly - just one more totally
gross task...

TOTALLY GROSS PURPLE HAND CLUB TASK

Go over to Margaret's house and
offer to play school with her.
That bossy-boots grouch is
always the teacher and the head
and you have to be the teacher's
pet. Ha ha!

RUDE RALPH: Oh no! He won't do that even to be in the Purple Hand!

LATER...

NEW NICK: I've done the totally gross task. Now, can I be in the Purple Hand Club?

HORRID HENRY AND RUDE RALPH: We'll think about it.

GREEDY GRAHAM'S FOOD FUN

Graham always has loads of sweets. He'd be a brilliant member of the Purple Hand Club. Graham, do you know any good dares?

GREEDY GRAHAM'S DARES

- Eat a chocolate bar using a knife and fork.

Not fair!

- Eat a whole doughnut without licking your lips once.

- Eat an apple in just ten bites. You can leave the stalk and core if you want.

Apples - yeuch!

- Eat a muffin without using your hands.

FOOD FIGHTS

- Find out who can fit the most marshmallows in their mouth at once.

- Float some apples in a bucket of water, and see who can fish the most out with their mouth.

Not more apples! Gross!

- Find out who can eat the most cream crackers in one minute, without having a drink of water.

Are all your dares about food?

- Move twenty chocolates from one plate to another using a straw. Race with a friend to see who can do it the quickest.

GREEDY GRAHAM: Hint - you could always eat the chocolates afterwards!

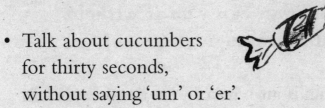

- Talk about cucumbers for thirty seconds, without saying 'um' or 'er'.

That's easy-peasy! Cucumbers are gross and green and ... um ... er ...

GREEDY GRAHAM: Here's one for you, Henry. Stand with your back against a wall, with your feet together and the backs of your heels touching the wall. I'll put this chocolate bar about thirty centimetres

in front of you. Now try to pick
up the chocolate without moving
your feet or bending your knees.
I bet you can't do it without
falling over.

That's not fair! It's impossible!
Forget the dares, tell us some
jokes.

GREEDY GRAHAM'S JOKES

Waiter, do you serve fish?
Sit down, sir, we serve anybody.

Brainy Brian: Miss Battle-Axe, I've got a
bone stuck in my throat.
Miss Battle-Axe: Are you choking?
Brainy Brian: No, I'm serious.

Waiter, this egg is bad.
Don't blame me, I only laid the table.

Waiter, will my pizza be long?
No, sir, it'll be round.

How do you stop someone
stealing fast food?
Fit a burger alarm.

What did the teddy say when
he was offered pudding?
No, thanks, I'm stuffed.

Why do tigers eat raw meat?
Because they can't cook.

Why do the French like to eat snails?
Because they don't like fast food!

**So you've
eaten at
Restaurant Le
Posh too!**

AEROBIC AL'S ATHLETIC DARES AND JOKES

AEROBIC AL: I know a lot of great dares and I dare you to try them. If you practise every day you might get to be almost as good as me!

- Balance a cup of water on your head and throw a ball into a hula hoop – at the same time.

AEROBIC AL: I won a medal for being best at this.

- Jump on one leg for twenty seconds with both hands on your head.

AEROBIC AL: I can do this for much longer than twenty seconds, but I thought I'd better make it easy for you.

- Do twenty star jumps, singing nursery rhymes at the same time.

- Balance a ball on a tennis racket and walk down the street.

These dares are as bad as PE at school! We don't do stuff like that in the Purple Hand Club – we watch loads of TV and scoff crisps and sweets.

AEROBIC AL: What about these fun dares then?

AEROBIC AL'S DARING DARES

- When you're at the swimming pool, shout, 'Look out for the shark!' then quickly leap out of the pool.
- Knock on your neighbour's front door and run away very fast.

That's more like it. Especially since Frog-Face Margaret is my next-door-neighbour. Tee hee!

- Kick as many footballs as you can over your next-door-neighbour's fence before they spot you.

Even better if you accidentally on purpose make one land on their head.

AEROBIC AL: I know some good sporty jokes too.

AEROBIC AL'S SPORTY JOKES

Why are bananas good at gymnastics?
Because they're great at doing the splits.

Why can't you play sports in the jungle?
Because of all the cheetahs.

Why did the golfer wear two pairs of pants?
In case he got a hole-in-one!

What's a waiter's best sport?
Tennis, because he is good at serving.

What has twenty-two legs and goes, 'Crunch, crunch, crunch'?
A football team eating crisps.

What do runners do when they forget something?
They jog their memories!

HORRID HENRY'S MONEY-MAKING SCHEMES

RUDE RALPH: What did you get for Christmas, Henry?

A drumkit. It's the best present I've ever had.

RUDE RALPH: Why?

My mum pays me not to play it!

HORRID HENRY'S MARVELLOUS MONEY-MAKING IDEAS

 Offer to sell Moody Margaret's Secret Club password to anyone who'll pay a pound.

 **PERFECT PETER: I know Margaret's Secret Club password, and I know the Purple Hand password too. It's...**

We've changed the password. Nah nah ne nah nah. Go back to the girls' book, slimy toad.

PERFECT PETER: Mum! Henry called me a slimy toad!

MUM: Henry! Don't be horrid!

 Set up a stall and sell all your old baby toys at top prices. Help yourself to your wormy worm brother's good toys. He's got far too many.

 Tell your parents that you're going to be perfect for a whole day – but only if they pay.

PERFECT PETER: That's not fair. I'm always perfect, and they don't pay me.

Get lost, toady toad.

 Offer to do the hoovering for your mum if she pays you. When she's out of the room, turn on the hoover, then settle down in a comfy chair with your favourite comic.

 Hide the TV remote control. Suggest to your parents that they pay a pound to whoever finds it. Then – yippee! – it just happens to be you.

 Get your mum to pay you for eating all your vegetables. She'll be so delighted you're going to eat healthily that she'll agree. Then, at tea time, when no one's looking, sneak the vegetables under the table, into your pockets and later into the bin.

Offer to take the dog for a walk for a
pound. Set off at a brisk pace, then as
soon as you're out of sight of the
house, find a bench and read the
comic that you've got hidden up
your t-shirt.

 Collect all the fruit and vegetables
from your kitchen and set up a stall
outside your house, with a poster
reading – 'Home-Grown Organic
Fruit and Veg'.

And best of all, your mum won't be able to make you eat any horrible green vegetables – because you'll have sold them all.

 Tell your friends that you can make coins vanish. When they hand over their money, sneak it into your pockets, then shout, 'Abracadabra! It's magic – your money has vanished!' When they ask you to make it reappear, just say you haven't learned that part of the trick yet.

BEEFY BERT GETS BAMBOOZLED

Bert, do you know any good tricks or dares?

BEEFY BERT: I dunno.

Do you know any good jokes?

BEEFY BERT: I dunno.

I'd better tell you my jokes then.

HORRID HENRY'S JOKES

How do you baffle Beefy Bert?
Put him in a round room and tell him
to sit in the corner.

What did Beefy Bert call his zebra?
Spot.

How do you catch a squirrel?
Climb up a tree and act like a nut.

**MOODY MARGARET :
Don't even think you
can join the Secret
Club, Bert. You need to
be clever to be a member
of my club.**

**He doesn't want to join your
girly club, do you, Bert?**

BEEFY BERT: I dunno.

MORE DARES FOR BEEFY BERT

- Run around wearing socks on your hands, trousers for a shirt and a shirt for trousers for three minutes.

- Sing 'I'm a little Teapot' and do all the actions.

- Stick out your tongue and touch your nose.

PSST! I never said you had to touch your nose with your tongue. Ha ha. You can stick out your tongue – and touch your nose with a finger!

BEEFY BERT: ??!!??

A BUZZING BALLOON TRICK TO BAFFLE BEEFY BERT

Here's a trick to keep Beefy Bert baffled for hours:

- Blow up a balloon, but don't tie up the end.

- Place the end of the balloon between the door and the doorframe and close the door quickly to hold the balloon.

- When Bert opens the door, the balloon will whiz all over the room – and Bert won't have any idea where it's come from!

RUDE RALPH'S RUDEST JOKES EVER

RUDE RALPH: I'll beat the stupid girls' club easily with my rude and rotten jokes.

MOODY MARGARET: Oh no, you won't.

RUDE RALPH: Bet I will.

MOODY MARGARET: Go on then. I dare you.

First man: My dog's got no nose.
Second man: How does he smell?
First man: Awful.

**MOODY
MARGARET: Boo!**

*Why do girls wear
make-up
and perfume?*
Because they're ugly
and they smell.

**MOODY MARGARET:
I think you mean
that BOYS are
ugly and smelly!**

*RUDE RALPH: Margaret eats like
a bird.*
HORRID HENRY: You mean she hardly
eats a thing?
*RUDE RALPH:
No, she eats slugs
and worms.*

MOODY MARGARET: NO, I DON'T!

Have you heard about Margaret? She isn't pretty and she isn't ugly.
She's pretty ugly!

MOODY MARGARET: HA HA HA. Not!

What do you call a girl with a carrot stuck in each ear?
Anything, she can't hear you.

NEW NICK'S FINAL TASKS

MOODY MARGARET: Nick is really nice. He's not horrible and smelly like the Purple Hand Club. Nick, you can be in the Secret Club if you want.

NEW NICK: Oh no! Not the girls' club! Please let me in the Purple Hand. I'll do anything you ask.

THREE MORE TERRIBLE TASKS FOR NICK BY ORDER OF THE PURPLE HAND LEADER

Henry

1. Wear a pair of girl's knickers to school and get through the day without anyone finding out.

2. Tell us some good jokes.

NEW NICK'S JOKES

What kind of dog smells of onions?
A hot dog.

What do you call a mean-looking green thing with long hairy legs.
I don't know.
Neither do I, but one of them has just gone down your jumper.

What's yellow on the inside and green on the outside?
A banana dressed up as a cucumber.

What lies in a pram and wobbles?
A jellybaby.

What do you call a sleeping bull?
  A bulldozer.

How do you describe a lazy skeleton?
  Bone idle.

3. Go over to Moody
Margaret's book and
give her a bunch of
flowers. But hide a fat
juicy worm inside
them! Tee hee!

**NEW NICK: Done it.
You should have heard
Margaret scream when
the worm leaped out at
her.**

MOODY MARGARET: You disgusting frogface! I HATE YOU!

NEW NICK: Mission accomplished. And I've got a bag of Big Boppers, some fizzywizz drinks and lots of gumballs.

HENRY AND RALPH: Welcome to the Purple Hand Club!

THE PURPLE HAND RULES OK!

Purple Hand rules OK! We've got all the best dares and all the best jokes.

MOODY MARGARET: That's rubbish! If you want to find out what a proper dare is come on over to my book...

No more Mr Nice Guy! This time it's war. On guard, Margaret. The Purple Hand has dares for all of the Secret Club and any other gruesome girls. If you fail, Purple Hand wins.

LAZY LINDA has to run down the street in her pyjamas – in the morning.

CLEVER CLARE has to get all her spellings wrong in the next spelling test.

SINGING SORAYA has to go through a whole day without singing a note.

GORGEOUS GURINDER has to wear Perfect Peter's clothes all day.

FIERY FIONA has to spend an hour not getting angry or annoyed once.

SOUR SUSAN has to smile sweetly for a whole day.

You're going to lose. You're going to lose. Nah na ne nah nah.

MOODY MARGARET: What's my dare then? Bet you can't think of anything I can't do better than anyone else.

I dare you to let me be Captain Hook next time we play pirates and not moan about it.

MOODY MARGARET: Let you play with my hook? No way! Walk the plank, you pongy pants pimple.

The enemy has retreated! The Purple Hand triumphs again. My club's the best, and my book's the best too. Read on for the offical, top secret results ...

Top Secret Results

	SECRET CLUB	PURPLE HAND
Dares/Tricks	-5,000	80,000
Jokes	-10,000	1,000,000

RESULT: The Secret Club loses. **Purple Hand is the BEST!** Now it's your turn to award points for the dares, tricks and jokes in this book:

DARES/TRICKS	...../10
JOKES	...../10
GRAND TOTAL	...../20

When you've read *Moody Margaret Strikes Back*, fill in your score for that book too. Which book came out on top?

HORRID HENRY'S DOUBLE DARES	...../20
MOODY MARGARET STRIKES BACK	...../20

HORRID HENRY BOOKS

Visit Horrid Henry's website at
www.horridhenry.co.uk for competitions, games,
downloads and a monthly newsletter!